DOUBLE-DECKER
DOUBLE-DECKER
DOUBLE-DECKER
BUS

by Patty Wolcott
illustrated by
Bob Barner

x W
yellow

♠ Addison-Wesley

"To all children who are learning to read"

FIRST READ-BY-MYSELF BOOKS
by PATTY WOLCOTT

Beware of a Very Hungry Fox
The Cake Story
Double-Decker, Double-Decker, Double-Decker Bus
The Dragon and the Wild Fandango
The Forest Fire
I'm Going to New York to Visit the Queen
The Marvelous Mud Washing Machine
My Shadow and I
Pickle Pickle Pickle Juice
Super Sam and the Salad Garden
Tunafish Sandwiches
Where Did That Naughty Little Hamster Go?

Text Copyright © 1980 by Patty Wolcott
Illustrations Copyright © 1980 by Bob Barner
All Rights Reserved
Addison-Wesley Publishing Company, Inc.
Reading, Massachusetts 01867
Printed in the United States of America
ABCDEFGHIJK-WZ-89876543210

Library of Congress Cataloging in Publication Data

Wolcott, Patty.
  Double-decker, double-decker, double-decker bus.
  SUMMARY: A youngster builds a double-decker bus.
  [1. Buses—Fiction] I. Barner, Bob. II. Title.
PZ7.W8185DO   [E]   79-23085
ISBN 0-201-08735-9

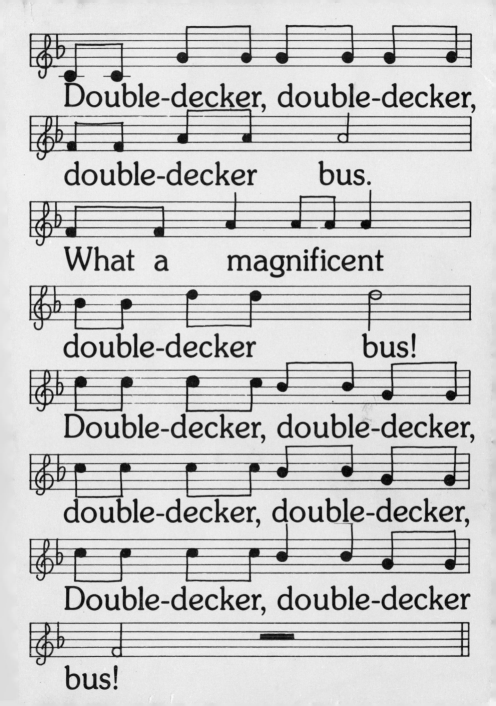

Double-decker, double-decker,

double-decker   bus.

What a   magnificent

double-decker   bus!

Double-decker, double-decker,

double-decker, double-decker,

Double-decker, double-decker

bus!